LEGO STAR WARS

YODA IN EXILE

CONTENTS

INTRODUCTION

One of the most mysterious and knowledgeable individuals in the galaxy, Yoda has lived for over 900 years. His incredible power with the force, and prowess with a lightsaber are matched only by his vast wisdom and compassion. Across the galaxy, Yoda's influence is felt through the friends he inspires and his enemies that fear him.

Before the end of the Republic, Yoda was the leader of the Jedi Order. He survived Order 66—an order given by Chancellor Palpatine that wiped out most of the Jedi. To escape the tyranny of the Empire, Yoda now lives in a hut on the forgotten swamp planet of Dagobah. Yoda waits to teach and train a new Padawan—who Yoda hopes will bring balance to the force by ending the reign of the evil Darth Sidious.

This is Yoda's story.

WHERE DOES YODA COME FROM?

Yoda is not the only member of his **species** to become a **Jedi**. Others are known, including the female **Yaddle**, who also served on the **Jedi Council**.

IT'S A QUESTION that many of his friends and enemies have asked. All that is known of Yoda's homeworld is that its inhabitants are green-skinned and short in stature, with very long lifespans and a high sensitivity to the Force. So where does he really come from? Everybody has a different theory!

I JUST THOUGHT YODA CAME FROM THE SWAMPS OF DAGOBAH WHERE I MET HIM. WHO KNEW HE HAD BEEN ON ADVENTURES ALL OVER THE GALAXY BEFORE THAT?

TELLING I AM NOT!

LUKE SKYWALKER

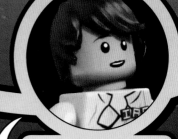

YOUNG HAN SOLO

I FIGURE HE COMES FROM THE PLANET OF CRANKY LITTLE GREEN GUYS, WHERE EVERYBODY TALKS FUNNY AND HAS A STRANGE SENSE OF HUMOR.

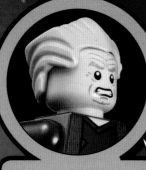

CHANCELLOR PALPATINE

WHEREVER HE COMES FROM, I HOPE THERE AREN'T ANY MORE OF HIM OUT THERE.

MACE WINDU

THE OTHER COUNCIL MEMBERS AND I ARE ALWAYS TRYING TO GET HIM TO TELL US WHERE HE COMES FROM, BUT HE WON'T SAY. I THINK HE LIKES ALL THE ATTENTION.

QUI-GON JINN

CLONE TROOPER

YODA NEVER SAID ANYTHING ABOUT HIS HOME PLANET DURING MY TRAINING. IT MADE ME WONDER IF IT HAD BEEN DESTROYED A LONG TIME AGO ...

HE'S A LITTLE GREEN LIZARD GUY, SO MAYBE HE'S FROM TATOOINE WHERE THOSE DEWBACKS COME FROM. THEY'RE GREEN LIZARDS TOO, RIGHT?

C-3PO

CHEWBACCA

AOOOGH ROOAAAR GRAAGH RUH.*

I AM FLUENT IN MORE THAN SIX MILLION FORMS OF COMMUNICATION, BUT AS FAR AS I AM CONCERNED, MASTER YODA IS ENTIRELY UNIQUE IN THE GALAXY!

* TRANSLATION: I KNOW WHERE HE'S FROM, BUT I'M NOT TELLING.

YODA'S WISDOM

YODA ISN'T THE BIGGEST Jedi Master around, but he is definitely one of the wisest. Although his way of speaking can sometimes be a little hard to follow, a Padawan who pays close attention to Yoda's teachings will become a great Jedi Knight.

"**FEAR** IS THE PATH TO THE **DARK SIDE**. **FEAR** LEADS TO **ANGER**. **ANGER** LEADS TO **HATE**. **HATE** LEADS TO **SUFFERING**."

"Do. Or do not. There is no try."

"**WARS** NOT MAKE ONE **GREAT**."

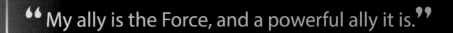

"My ally is the Force, and a powerful ally it is."

"**ADVENTURE.** EXCITEMENT. A **JEDI** CRAVES NOT THESE THINGS."

"When 900 years old you reach, look as good you will not."

"A **JEDI** USES THE FORCE FOR **KNOWLEDGE** AND **DEFENSE**, NEVER FOR **ATTACK**."

"Smaller in number we are, but larger in mind."

"**EVERYTHING** YOU FEAR TO **LOSE**, **LEARN** TO LET GO OF YOU **MUST**."

"To answer power with power, the Jedi way this is not."

"IF ONCE YOU START DOWN THE **DARK PATH**, FOREVER WILL IT DOMINATE YOUR **DESTINY**."

YODA'S ALLIES

Holoprojector

Starship linkage arms

SECRET WEDDING
When Anakin Skywalker and Padmé Amidala ignore the Jedi Codeand get married, they exchange droids. R2-D2 becomes Anakin's assistant, and C-3PO Padmé's. The two droids keep the secret so well that even Yoda doesn't know about the wedding!

DATA FILE

 HOMEWORLD: NABOO

CREATION DATE: AROUND 33 BBY

DROID TYPE: R2-SERIES ASTROMECH DROID

BUILT BY: INDUSTRIAL AUTOMATON

EQUIPMENT: BUZZ SAW, FUSION WELDER, THRUSTER JETS, AND MORE

R2-D2

This brave beeping and buzzing little droid is always ready to help his friends, and often notices what others miss. He may even suspect the truth about Chancellor Palpatine … but if so, he hasn't had any luck telling anyone!

Barrel-like body filled with hidden tools and gadgets

Recharge coupling

R2-D2 AND C-3PO

YODA HAS MET a lot of droids in his long lifetime, but none quite like this unusual pair. "Artoo" and "Threepio" have had adventures across the galaxy, somehow ending up right in the middle of the action no matter where they go.

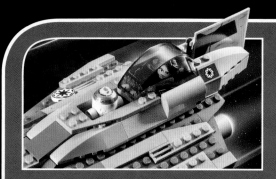

CO-PILOT
As an astromech droid, R2-D2 is programmed to repair and navigate starships. His gadgets, inventiveness, and heroism often save the day in the heat of battle.

Class-6 escape pod

ESCAPE TO TATOOINE
While Yoda is dwelling as a hermit on Dagobah, R2-D2 and C-3PO get caught up in yet another battle for the fate of the galaxy. Artoo becomes a key agent of the Rebel Alliance and the guardian of the plans to the Empire's ultimate weapon: the Death Star! He leads C-3PO on a journey through the desert of Tatooine to deliver the plans to Obi-Wan Kenobi.

OH, NO. I'M NOT GOING ANYWHERE UNTIL YOU PUT THIS POD BACK TOGETHER AND FLY US OUT OF HERE!

WHEE-OO BLEEP!

Photoreceptor

Vocabulator

Exposed connection wires

C-3PO
A protocol droid who knows more than 6 million forms of communication, C-3PO is proper, polite, and constantly worried. He never asked for excitement, but it keeps finding him. All things considered, he'd much rather relax in a nice hot oil bath!

SUBSTITUTE TEACHER
Since he was first assembled by Anakin, poor C-3PO has seemed to face one peril after another. Still, he's rarely encountered as dangerous a mission as having to substitute-teach Yoda's class of unruly Jedi trainees ... not to mention drive their school bus!

DATA FILE

HOMEWORLD: TATOOINE

CREATION DATE: 112 BBY, REBUILT 32 BBY

DROID TYPE: 3PO-SERIES PROTOCOL DROID

BUILT BY: CYBOT GALACTICA (REBUILT BY ANAKIN SKYWALKER)

EQUIPMENT: NONE

JABBA THE HUTT

THE INFAMOUS JABBA the Hutt is a powerful slug-like crime lord with a palace full of tough alien henchmen. Jabba would love to have some Jedi lightsabers of his own—even if he has to make the sound effects himself!

Stone and durasteel construction

<I WOULD PAY A GREAT BOUNTY FOR A WORKING LIGHTSABER.> *

* TRANSLATED FROM HUTTESE

Jabba's assistant, Bib Fortuna

Hookah pipe

I'D BE HAPPY TO JUST GET A DAY OFF!

Twi'lek dancer Oola

Salacious Crumb, a Kowakian monkey-lizard

Bounty hunter Boushh

Gamorrean guard watchman

Gun stash

Fortified palace entrance

JABBA'S PALACE

Jabba's palace lies on the edge of the Northern Dune Sea on Tatooine. It's not easy to sneak inside, but when Yoda's students' lightsabers end up in Jabba's slimy clutches, that's just what the young Padawans have to do!

Yoda once sent **Anakin** Skywalker and his apprentice Ahsoka to rescue Jabba's **kidnapped** son **Rotta**. The act earned the Republic permission to fly its **ships** through Hutt space … and gained Yoda the **respect** of the mighty Jabba.

RANCOR PIT

Beneath a trap door in Jabba's throne room is the lair of the fearsome Rancor. Jabba's favorite sport is dropping unwelcome visitors into this pit, where they must battle for survival against the hulking monster—or else find a very good hiding place, and fast!

Twi'lek head-tails

Pointed teeth

BIB FORTUNA

Bib Fortuna is a Twi'lek from the planet Ryloth, and is Jabba's assistant, majordomo, and occasional sail barge pilot. Despite his extra-big brain, he is surprisingly easy to fool—both by Force mind tricks and by droid distractions that help Jedi younglings creep past!

DATA FILE

- **HOMEWORLD:** NAL HUTTA
- **BIRTH DATE:** 600 BBY
- **POSITION:** CRIME LORD
- **CLAN:** DESILIJIC
- **WEIGHT:** 1,358 KG (2,994 POUNDS)

YODA'S GALAXY

THE GALAXY IS A BIG PLACE,
but you can see quite a lot of it if you
live to be almost 900 years old.
Yoda has visited many worlds on his
interplanetary adventures—some of which
he'd like to return to more than others!

NABOO

"A lovely vacation spot this is.
From Naboo many well-known
beings come: Senator Amidala,
Supreme Chancellor Palpatine,
and the famous Gungan Jar Jar
Binks. Enjoyed I did, going for a
refreshing swim to the Gungan
city, and the ducks I fed by the
Royal Palace. Recommend
it I do, but for Sith Lords,
watch out you should."

Naboo

GEONOSIS

GEONOSIS

"Like bugs and battle droids, you do?
Then to Geonosis go you should.
With a large group of new clone friends
here I came, and an old student bumped
into I did. Had to leave in a hurry Count
Dooku did, heh heh! Heard I have a new
Sith Academy setting up Dooku is.
Drop in again soon I may."

CORUSCANT

"Noise. Traffic. Politics. Care for these things I do not. But here is the Jedi Temple, so here too am I! One giant city the planet Coruscant is, capital of the Republic. Important decisions the Jedi Council makes, such as which younglings to train and where to go for lunch. Not easy it is to get 12 Jedi Masters to agree!"

HOTH

HOTH

"For contemplation and self-discovery a good place the ice world Hoth is. Mostly your own freezing point discover you will. Very scenic the glaciers and caves are, if hungry wampas you avoid. Send the Padawans here on their next field trip, I shall. Meet any dangerous clone warriors, I hope they will not!"

TATOOINE

"To this planet of twin suns I once traveled. Badly sunburnt I got (not well do green and red skin mix!). In Mos Eisley, stolen my luggage was. Smelled like bantha fodder, my hotel room did. Suggest visiting here I do not."

Greetings from Tatooine

YODA VS.

THERE ARE TWO SIDES to the Force. The light side is an ally to Yoda, but the dark side poses great danger. Darth Sidious is the most powerful dark side follower. He and Yoda are matched in strength, but draw on opposing sides of the Force.

THE PATH OF TRUTH AND GOODNESS, THE LIGHT SIDE IS.

THE LIGHT SIDE

Jedi spend their lives studying the light side of the Force. Through focus and meditation, they achieve inner balance and an enhanced awareness of the universe. The Force grants them great power and knowledge, which they use to uphold peace and justice in the galaxy.

■ WISDOM

■ COMPASSION

■ INNER STRENGTH

■ LOYALTY

■ JUSTICE

THE DARK SIDE

> BUT MY SIDE HAS COOL OUTFITS AND RED LIGHTSABERS!

THE DARK SIDE

For every light, there is a shadow. Those who cross over to the dark side of the Force are fueled by negative emotions such as greed and rage. The dark side offers them almost unlimited power— but this comes at a cost, damaging their bodies and even their minds.

- SECRET TEACHINGS
- PASSION
- TERRIFYING POWER
- JEALOUSY
- DESTRUCTION

THE EMPIRE

YODA GOES INTO HIDING as a dark new order rises to replace the Republic. The Empire rules the galaxy through oppression and fear, tightening its grip to crush all resistance and keep unhappy worlds under control.

Superlaser weapon

EMPEROR PALPATINE

With his true face revealed at last, the former Chancellor now reigns supreme as the Emperor. Yoda's greatest foe is enormously powerful in the dark side of the Force. His only weakness is his misguided belief that no one can stand against him.

Face and eyes distorted by dark side energies

The Emperor has no need for fancy clothing

A second Death Star is built after its predecessor was destroyed by Luke Skywalker and the Rebel Alliance.

DATA FILE

 HOMEWORLD: NABOO

 BIRTH DATE: 82 BBY

 RANK: EMPEROR

 TRAINED BY: DARTH PLAGUEIS

 WEAPON: FORCE LIGHTNING

For all of his **wisdom** and experience, even Yoda never **guesses** that the Emperor's **defeat** will come at the hands of **Darth Vader**.

STORMTROOPERS

Protected by suits of plastoid armor, the clones who once fought on Yoda's side in the Republic have become the Empire's army of obedient stormtroopers. If any of them are still loyal to their old Jedi generals, they definitely hide it well!

DARTH VADER

As the Emperor's right-hand man, the Sith Lord once known as Anakin Skywalker has sworn to hunt down the last of the Jedi Knights. But soon there is another Jedi —because Yoda has trained Anakin's son, Luke Skywalker, to someday face his father.

Exposed internal structure

Red-bladed Sith lightsaber

Pressurized helmet

Chest control panel

Armor with built-in life support

THE DEATH STAR

The Empire's ultimate weapon, the Death Star is a moon-sized space station that can deconstruct a planet with a single blast. When the first Death Star destroys Alderaan, Yoda can sense the disturbance in the Force all the way on Dagobah.

DATA FILE

HOMEWORLD: TATOOINE

REBIRTH DATE: 19 BBY

RANK: SITH LORD

TRAINED BY: OBI-WAN KENOBI, EMPEROR PALPATINE

WEAPON: RED-BLADED LIGHTSABER

LUKE SKYWALKER

YODA HAS TRAINED many Jedi over the centuries. But few have been as important to the fate of the galaxy—or as challenging to teach—as the adventurous and brave young Luke Skywalker.

Anakin Skywalker's old lightsaber

FROM FARMBOY TO JEDI

The farmboy from Tatooine brings a new hope to the few surviving Jedi and the Rebel Alliance against the Empire. Yoda senses that the Force is strong in Luke, but his impatience and lack of discipline remind Yoda of Luke's long-lost father, Anakin.

DATA FILE

 HOMEWORLD: TATOOINE

 BIRTH DATE: 19 BBY

 RANK: JEDI MASTER

 TRAINED BY: OBI-WAN KENOBI AND YODA

 WEAPON: BLUE- AND LATER GREEN-BLADED LIGHTSABER

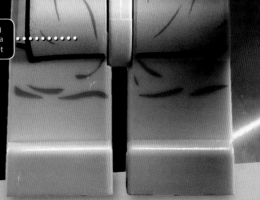

Loose-fitting clothing for a desert planet

MEETING YODA
Instructed by the spirit of Obi-Wan Kenobi, Luke travels to Dagobah in search of a great Jedi warrior to train him. But Luke is surprised to discover that the mysterious "Yoda" he seeks is a strange little green creature whose first lesson is that appearances can be deceiving.

PRINCESS LEIA

When Anakin Skywalker's twins are born, Yoda decides that they should be hidden and raised apart to keep them safe. While Luke is sent to Tatooine, his sister Leia becomes a princess of Alderaan. She is also a secret leader of the Rebel Alliance.

> "I'M LOOKING FOR A GREAT WARRIOR."
>
> LUKE TO YODA

CELEBRATED PILOT

Like his father, Luke's strong connection to the Force makes him a naturally skilled starfighter pilot. Thanks to this talent, the young Jedi is able to blow up the Death Star on his first flight in an X-wing fighter, saving the Rebel Alliance from destruction by the Empire!

R2-D2 in astromech socket

Laser cannon

S-foil wings open for combat

I SURE HOPE THE FORCE IS WITH ME RIGHT NOW!

Proton torpedo launcher

HAN SOLO

Roguish smuggler Han Solo was drawn into the fight against the Empire when his battered ship, the *Millennium Falcon*, was chartered by Luke and Obi-Wan. The ship was once a flying nightclub owned by Lindo Calrissian and his son Lando. Long ago, they gave Yoda a much-needed lift to the planet Kamino.

SOLO DUO

Han Solo and Yoda go way back. As a child, Han disguised himself as a Jedi Padawan named Ian, and the unlikely pair of heroes shared an action-packed outer space adventure.

Tree roots wrap around hut

YODA'S HUT

It may not be as luxurious as a Jedi Temple, but this humble hut has everything Yoda requires. Built into the base of a large tree, its walls are a mix of mud and parts from the escape pod that Yoda used to travel to Dagobah.

Entrance—watch your head!

HOME SWEET HOME, THIS IS!

Creeping vines grow everywhere

YODA AT HOME

Sleeping chamber

WELCOME TO DAGOBAH!

When you're the Empire's number one Most Wanted, it's the perfect place to hide out and wait for the galaxy's new hope to arrive. Who needs technology and civilization when you've got weeds, muck, and weird creatures to keep you company?

SECRET COMPARTMENT

Yoda took a few important Jedi relics with him on his flight from Coruscant. Among the most precious is his lightsaber. Yoda keeps his weapon safely hidden in a secret space underneath his small but cozy bed.

CAN YOU
LIFT AN

YES, IF YOU'RE IN TUNE with the Force! With the right mindset and training, a person can use this energy to accomplish incredible feats, from sensing the future to taming wild beasts. Luke Skywalker learns much about the Force from Yoda. He is surprised to discover that someone as small as the old Jedi Master can lift something as huge as an X-wing starfighter—just by raising his hand!

SURE, I CAN LIFT IT. I JUST NEED TO BUILD A REALLY BIG CRANE ...

Luke Skywalker

Closed S-foils

Who knows what hungry creatures lurk beneath the swamp's surface?

Landing gear is useless in sticky swamp muck.

X-WING? (WITHOUT TOUCHING IT?)

I COULD TOTALLY DO IT, BUT NOBODY EVER ASKS!

R2-D2

JUDGE ME BY MY SIZE, DO YOU? HAH! SEE WHAT I CAN DO!

CRASH COURSE

On Dagobah, Yoda has only a short time to teach Luke to become a Jedi Knight in order to save the galaxy from the Emperor's evil plans. Yoda does his best to help Luke to understand how to feel the Force, how to ignore distractions, and … how to move rocks while balancing upside down with his teacher standing on his foot! Nobody said Jedi training is easy.

Clinging Dagobah marsh weeds

What else can the **Force** do? Someone who is skilled in it can **jump** amazing distances, block blaster **shots** with a lightsaber, and **influence** the thoughts of small-minded bad guys!

WHAT IS YODA'S LEGACY?

AFTER 900 YEARS, age finally catches up with Yoda. But even after he becomes one with the Force, Yoda and his teachings continue to affect the fate of the galaxy. Yoda's final student, Luke Skywalker, succeeds in defeating the power of the Empire, bringing an end to the Emperor's tyrannical rule and at last restoring balance to the Force.

THE FINAL BATTLE
On the second Death Star, Luke faces Darth Vader in a titanic lightsaber duel. With the wisdom he has gained from Yoda, Luke reaches out to his father, who has long been buried beneath Vader's mask and armor. Freed from the dark side, Anakin Skywalker destroys Emperor Palpatine, and with him the might of the Sith.

Darth Vader must choose between his allegiance to the Emperor and his son

JOIN ME, MY SON.

NO. YOU JOI ME, FATHER!

New lightsaber constructed by Luke

Mechanical hand

Circular viewport into space

LOOK, SOMEONE JOIN SOMEBODY ALREADY!

Emperor's throne

A **Jedi's** passing is not necessarily the **end**. Although his physical form disappears, Yoda **continues** to watch over Luke as a **Force spirit**.

Imperial throne room at the top of a 100-story tower

GONE BUT NEVER FORGOTTEN

Luke goes on to become a great Jedi Master. He builds a new Jedi Order for the reborn New Republic, always guided and inspired by the lessons of his wise old teacher. Through the Holocron recordings stored in the Jedi Library on Coruscant, young Jedi will continue to learn from Yoda's knowledge and experience for many generations to come.

GLOSSARY

BATTLE DROID
A Separatist robot designed for combat.

BOUNTY HUNTER
Someone who is hired to track down or destroy people or objects for money.

CHANCELLOR
The title given to the head of the Republic.

DARK SIDE
The evil side of the Force that feeds off negative emotions.

DEATH STAR
An enormous Imperial battle station, which has enough firepower to destroy an entire planet.

DROID
A robot. Droids come in many shapes and sizes and serve a variety of duties.

EMPIRE
A tyrannical power that rules the galaxy under the leadership of Emperor Palpatine, a Sith Lord.

EMPEROR
Ruler of the Empire.

FORCE
The energy that flows through all living things. It can be used for good or evil.

FORCE LIGHTNING
Deadly rays of blue energy used as a weapon.

FORCE PUSH
A blast of energy that a Force-user can use to knock over an opponent.

HOLOCRON
An ancient device that contains large amounts of data. It is activated through use of the Force.

JEDI
A member of the Jedi Order who studies the light side of the Force.

JEDI COUNCIL
Twelve senior Jedi who meet to make important decisions.

JEDI KNIGHT
A full member of the Jedi Order who has completed all of their training.

JEDI MASTER
An experienced and high-ranking Jedi who has demonstrated great skill and dedication.

LIGHTSABER
A sword-like weapon with a blade of pure energy that is used by Jedi and Sith.

LIGHT SIDE
The good side of the Force that brings peace and justice.

PADAWAN
A young Jedi apprentice who is in training to become a full-fledged Jedi Knight.

REBEL ALLIANCE
The organization that resists and fights the Empire.

REPUBLIC
The democratic government that rules many planets in the galaxy.

SENATE
The government of the Republic. It is made up of senators from all over the galaxy.

SENATOR
A person who acts as a representative for their planet in the Senate.

SITH
An ancient sect of Force-sensitives who seek to use the dark side of the Force to gain power.

YOUNGLING
A Force-sensitive child who joins the Jedi Order to be trained in the Jedi arts.

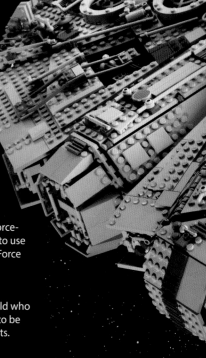

Penguin
Random
House

Senior Editors Elizabeth Dowsett
and Helen Murray
Editor Matt Jones
Senior Designer Lisa Sodeau
Designer Jon Hall
Senior DTP Designer David McDonald
Senior Producer Lloyd Robertson
Managing Editor Simon Hugo
Design Manager Guy Harvey
Creative Manager Sarah Harland
Art Director Lisa Lanzarini
Publisher Julie Ferris
Publishing Director Simon Beecroft

Additional photography by Gary Ombler

Dorling Kindersley would like to thank: Randi Sørensen and Louise Weiss
Borup at the LEGO Group; Jonathan W. Rinzler, Troy Alders, Rayne Roberts,
Pablo Hidalgo, and Leland Chee at Lucasfilm; Lisa Stock for editorial
assistance and John Goldsmid for design assistance.

First published in the United States in 2015 by
DK Publishing, 345 Hudson Street, New York, New York, 10014

Contains material previously published in
LEGO® Star Wars®: The Yoda Chronicles (2013)

004-284485-Feb/15

Page design copyright © 2015 Dorling Kindersley Limited
A Penguin Random House Company

ISBN: 978-5-0010-1300-6

Color reproduction by Alta Image, UK
Printed and bound in China

www.dk.com
www.LEGO.com/starwars

A WORLD OF IDEAS:
SEE ALL THERE IS TO KNOW